What I Know

Draw, write or do both to show three things that you know about feeding and exercise.

What I know

What Do You Need to Survive?

1. What do humans and other animals need to survive and be healthy?

   Write a message in the bottle about what you need to survive and stay healthy.

   _____

   _____

   _____

Staying Alive

Humans have basic needs for staying alive.

1   **Name three things that you need to stay alive.**

   1 _____

   2 _____

   3 _____

In addition to basic needs for survival, we may want other things, for example to be safe and warm.

2   **Draw two other things that are useful to help you stay alive.**

1	2

3   **Can we survive longer without water or without food?**

_____

Shipwrecked!

Imagine that you are shipwrecked on this desert island.

1   How would you meet your basic needs of food and water?

   _____
   _____

2   What else would you need to do?

   _____
   _____

Where Does our Food Come From? Classifying

Classify (sort) the foods into groups of where they come from: plant, animal or both.
Record your work in the table.
Think of some more foods and add them too.

rice

mutton stew

orange juice

pancake

cheese

dates

banana smoothie

milk

chicken

Plant	Animal	Both plant and animal

Where Does our Food Come From? Milk

Food often needs to be changed in some way before we can eat it.

1 Put the diagrams in the correct order to show the journey of milk from cow to supermarket.
   The first one has been done for you.

A

B

C

D

1 __C__

2 ____

3 ____

4 ____

Food Packaging

1. Write the first four ingredients from the cookie label in order. Add where they come from: plant, animal or both.

Chocolate Chip Cookie

Ingredients
Flour
Sugar
Butter
Eggs
Chocolate chips

1 _____

2 _____

3 _____

4 _____

2. Look at your own food labels. Choose one, write what it is (e.g. chicken soup) and write the first four ingredients. Are they plant, animal or both?

My food label is _____

	Ingredient	Plant, animal or both?
1		
2		
3		
4		

Animal Diets

Different kinds of animals eat different types of food.

1 What do these animals eat?

Animal	What it eats
sheep	
hedgehog	
owl	

2 Choose one of the animals from the table.

Draw it and label it as a carnivore, a herbivore or an omnivore.

Food Chains

1. Draw the arrows for this food chain.
   Make sure they are pointing in the correct direction to show where the energy 'goes into'.

| Grass | | Slug | | Frog |

2. Draw a food chain for animals where you live.

Science Skills

Investigate it!

Plan an investigation to compare which food the birds near school prefer.

Draw which type of foods you will use.

The four types of food I am going to investigate are:

1 Which do you think will be the most popular food for the birds? Why?

_____
_____

Feeding and Exercise

2 How will you make the investigation as fair as possible so you can compare the foods?

- We should _____
  _____

- We should _____
  _____

- We should _____
  _____

Carry out the investigation to see what happens.

3 Which food was most popular?

_____

4 Were you right when you chose which food you thought would be most popular? Explain why.

_____
_____

Lifestyle Choices: Food

It is important to eat a diet with the right amount of different foods to have a healthy lifestyle.

1. Draw and write to show what might happen if you do not eat the right amount of different foods.

_____

_____

2. Which foods should you eat only a small amount of? Why?

_____

_____

Lifestyle Choices: Exercise

1. Draw yourself doing your favourite type of exercise.

2. How does your body feel when you are exercising?

_____
_____

Be a Lifestyle Coach

Imagine that you are a lifestyle coach. You help people to improve their health and fitness.
What would you say about each of these?

1a Food: How much should we eat? What types of food?

1b Exercise: How much exercise and how often?

Food Safety

Food safety poster

Design a poster to show how to store, prepare and eat food safely.

What I Have Learned

1. Show what you have learned about the topics in the boxes below. You could write a sentence, draw a picture or do both.

Basic needs for survival	Feeding

Exercise	Food safety

2. Look at your first page in this workbook. What new things have you learned?

_____
_____